HEATHCLIFF
ALL AMERICAN

The funniest feline in America delights millions of fans every day as he appears in over 500 newspapers. You'll have a laugh a minute as Heathcliff tangles with the milkman, the cat show judge, the veterinarian and just about everyone else he runs into. If you're looking for some fun, look no further. Heathcliff is here!

HEATHCLIFF ALL AMERICAN!

by Geo Gately

JOVE BOOKS, NEW YORK

Originally included in the Tempo Books
collection *Heathcliff in Concert*.

HEATHCLIFF ALL AMERICAN

A Jove Book / published by arrangement with
Licensed Ventures, International.

PRINTING HISTORY
Special Book Club edition / April 1987

Jove Books are published by The Berkley Publishing Group,
200 Madison Avenue, New York, New York 10016.
The name "JOVE" and the "J" logo
are trademarks belonging to Jove Publications, Inc.

PRINTED IN THE UNITED STATES OF AMERICA

10   9   8   7   6   5   4   3   2   1

"IT MUST HAVE BEEN A MONSTER!"

"HEATHCLIFF!...WHERE'S MY TROMBONE?!"

"PROCEEDS FROM TONIGHT'S CONCERT WILL BE
DONATED TO THE DOGCATCHER'S RELIEF FUND!"

"THEY'VE DECORATED THEIR DOORWAY."

"LEMME KNOW IF
YE SPOT ANY TUNA."

"PHEW!...TALK ABOUT A SHOWER MASSAGE!!"

"ALL CLEAR!"

"LET ME KNOW IF HEATHCLIFF ANNOYS YOU."

"HEATHCLIFF'S BEEN CHASING A MOUSE ALL MORNING."

"....SO, THE BIG, BAD WOLF HUFFED AND PUFFED AND....

...I'LL TELL THE STORY!"

"I THINK THE PLACE IS HAUNTED,
AND SO DOES HEATHCLIFF!"

"I FINALLY GOT HIM TO ORGANIZE
HIS CAT FOOD COUPONS."

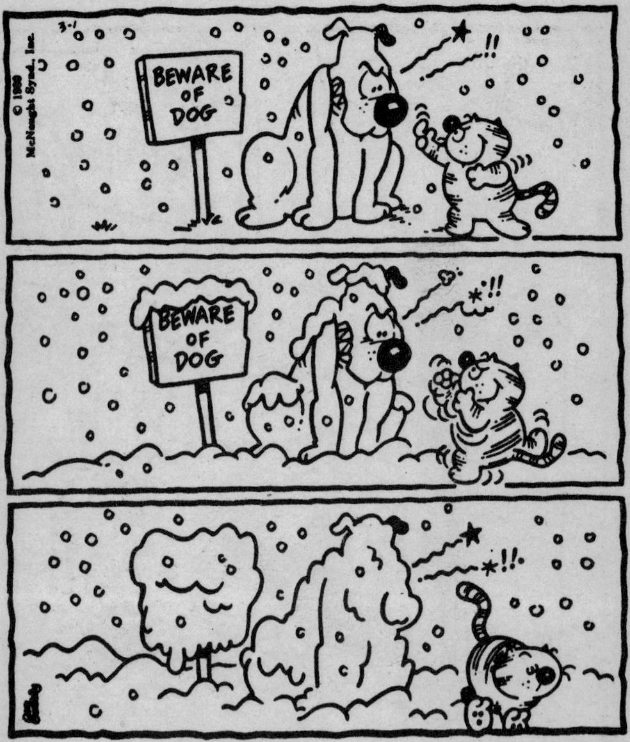
3-1
McNaught Synd., Inc.
BEWARE OF DOG
BEWARE OF DOG

"HE'S GOT HIMSELF A WOK!"

"MOVE ALONG, LAD.... NO LOITERING!"

"COME BACK WITH THAT FLOUNDER!"

"SNIFF...GOSH!...NOW THE POOR DOG IS IN
REAL TROUBLE!!"

"CONTESTANTS WILL REMAIN IN THEIR BOOTHS!"

"HE'S NOT HELPING THIS SITUATION ANY!"

"SEE THERE?...FIFI'S NOT AFRAID OF YOU!"

"HERE COMES OL' TWINKLETOES!"

"MISSED!"

"PRUNING EARLY THIS SPRING ?!"

"THE 'PHANTOM OF GARBAGE' STRIKES AGAIN!"

"COCK-A-DOODLE-DO!"

"YOU'RE UP EARLY THIS MORNING!"

"HAVE YE NEVER HEARD O' THE WEE LEPRECHAUNS?"

"NO, DEAR...HE IS NOT WITH THE 'WELCOME WAGON'."

"I DON'T THINK HE'S ADMIRING YOUR EASTER BONNET!"

"THERE WILL BE NO OVERNIGHT PAJAMA PARTY!"

"NOW AND THEN HE LEAVES HOME,
SO I KEEP HIS CLOTHES IN THE TRUNK."

"YOU'RE SUPPOSED TO GET YOUR WORKOUT
CHASING MICE!"

"PHEEW!...YOU SURE CAN CLIMB WHEN YOU WANT TO!"

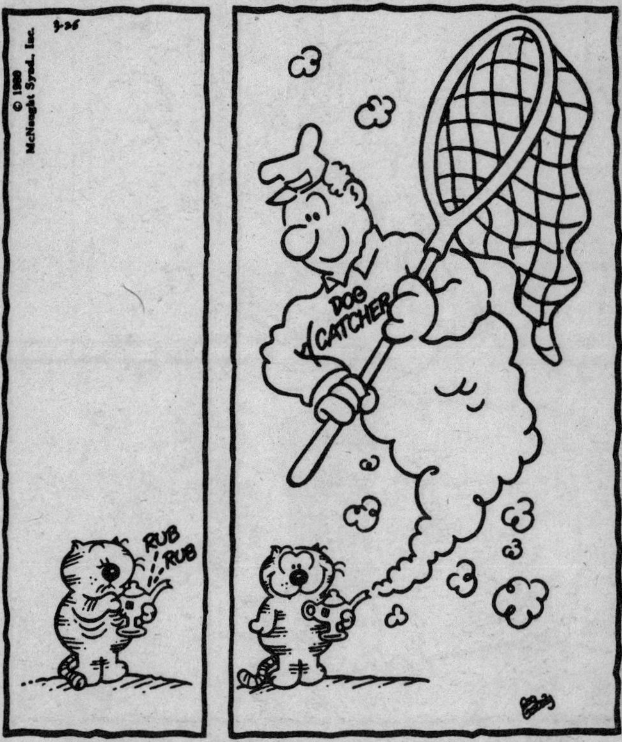
© 1980
McNaught Synd., Inc.
3-26
RUB RUB
DOG CATCHER

"I WISH YOU'D LEAVE YOUR BUSINESS PROBLEMS AT THE OFFICE."

"FOILED BY A SCRATCHING POST!"

"I'VE HAD ENOUGH OF YOUR HECKLING!"

"HIS CONTRACT GRANTS HIM SCRIPT APPROVAL."

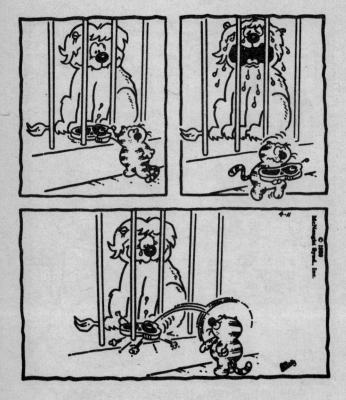

"NICE GOIN', SPIKE...YOU WENT THE DISTANCE!"

"THEY'RE BURYING THE 'HEATHCLIFF TIME CAPSULE'."

"COO, COO!"

"THAT'S A VERY PICTURESQUE MILK SPILL!"

"THAT'S A VERY SICK BIRD."

"SOMEBODY IS HAVING A GOOD LAUGH ABOUT SOMETHING!"

"HEATHCLIFF!...IS THAT THE TOP
OF THE CAKE DISH?"

"PLEASE WELCOME OUR NEWEST MEMBER, HEATHCLIFF...

...WHO HAS A VERY SERIOUS PROBLEM!"

"SOMEBODY THREW TAP SHOES!"

"WOULD YOU MIND......?!"

"I WISH HE WOULDN'T DIG UP THAT FRONT YARD!"

"...AND THEN, HALF WAY THROUGH THE BREAK IN,
YOU WERE APPREHENDED...."

"THERE'S ALWAYS A BRAWL WHEN
THE TUNA FLEETS IN TOWN!"

"THEY STOCKED THE LAKE WITH TROUT!...
IT'LL BE LIKE SHOOTING FISH IN A BARREL!"

"QUICK!...FOLLOW THAT BABY CARRIAGE!"

"IT CONTAINS NO CAT FOOD COUPONS!"

" DID YOUSE DROP A MILK BOTTLE, PAL ?!... "

"I WISH YOU'D STOP EXPERIMENTING
WITH THOSE MOUSESICLES!"

"SORRY ABOUT THAT, PROFESSOR!"

"80% OF ALL ACCIDENTS HAPPEN CLOSE TO HOME!"

"HE'S GETTING QUITE AN OVATION!"

" JUST A MOMENT THERE, 'BIRDIE'!"

"OH, NO, HEATHCLIFF!...DON'T LET THE AIR
OUT OF HIS TIRES!"

"THE HEATHCLIFF SEAL OF APPROVAL!"

"YOU COULD AT LEAST LET ME GET OUT
OF THE GARAGE!"

"WERE YOU AFTER THIS CLOCK AGAIN ?!"

"WHAT'S A COCKOO DOING IN THE BIRD BATH ?!"

"THERE'S A BIG REWARD IN THIS FOR YOU, FELLA!"

"FINGERPRINT HIM YOURSELF, SARGE!"

"YOU'RE SUPPOSED TO JUST *NUDGE* HIM
AWAY FROM THE DISH!"

"OH, OH!...HE'S PUT ON THE RUBBER GLOVES!"

"THIS ONE OF YOUR CREW ?!"

" HORS D'OEUVRES !! "

"CAN I SEE YOUR HUNTING LICENSE ?!"

"HE'S USING MY TROMBONE FOR A BIRD FEEDER!"

" JUST LET ME REACH THE GOVERNOR...
HE'LL GRANT ME A REPRIEVE."

"THE VET PUT YOU ON A BLAND DIET....
NO LOBSTER, NO PHEASANT, NO SHRIMP..."

"IT'S A SURE SIGN WE'RE IN FOR A COLD WINTER."

"I WISH THEY'D DO SOMETHING ABOUT
THESE POT HOLES!"

"HEATHCLIFF, YOU'RE A THIEVING SCOUNDREL!"

".... AND, SO'S YOUR OLD MAN!"

"AS YOUR VETERINARIAN, I RECOMMEND
'WHOOPEE CAT FOOD'...NOW WOULD YOU MIND
IF I CONTINUE WITH MY OWN SHOPPING?"

"I SEE YOUR DAD IS WEARING HIS CUT OFFS."

"HE'S PRACTICING HIS SLAM DUNK!"

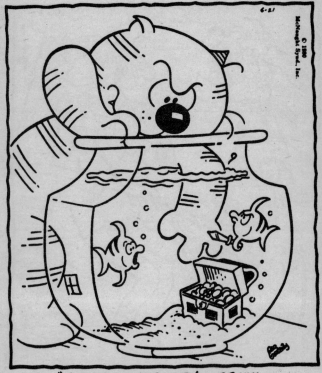

"FOR CRYING OUT LOUD!...LET HIM
HAVE THE TREASURE!"

"HEATHCLIFF!...SUPPER!"

"I WISH YOU WOULDN'T
COME DOWN THE CHIMNEY!"

"HELLO ?... HARBOR PATROL...."

"YOU KILLED A FRISBEE ?!"

"DEAL ME OUT!"

"YES...HIM !!"

"WE'RE READY FOR THE STAR."

"AREN'T YOU BEING A BIT ROUGH ON THE DEFENDANT, COUNSELOR?"

"MY LUNCH HOUR MUST BE OVER."

"WE WERE LOOKING AT CAMPERS."

"HE'S A LOT NEATER SINCE HE HIRED A BUS BOY."

"DID YOU THREATEN MY MUSIC TEACHER ?!"

"LOOKS LIKE A HERD OF CATTLE WENT THROUGH HERE!"

"HEATHCLIFF TOOK HIM INTO THE BETTING PARLOR."

"SOME THINGS I CAN'T SAVE."

"HE KNOWS I'M TICKLISH!"

"THERE'S BEEN A SLIGHT ERROR IN SHIPPING..."

"THE CHIEF SAYS HIS COLLECTION
CONSTITUTES A FIRE HAZARD."

"KITTY CAN'T WAIT...

...FOR DELICIOUS 'LIVER LUMPS'!"

" ON THIS SITE THE VALIANT HEATHCLIFF DIDST VANQUISH MUGGSY FABER'S DOG SPIKE AND..."

"BUT THERE'S NO CEMENT ON HIS PAWS!"

"THIS ONE HARDLY FITS IN THE NET!"

"SOMEONE KNOCKED OVER THE BAIT SHOP!"

"HE'S WORKING WITH A BEAVER!"